This book belongs to

....

....

This journey would not have been possible without some
amazing and talented individuals who we have been
blessed to have met.

Illustrations by Josefina Luna
Designed by Vanessa Fernandes
Wallpaper by Josefina Luna

ISBN 978-0-6457461-2-9

Join Jackson's Journey further at
www.joinjacksonsjourney.com.au

There are many different views on best practice leadership.
The strategies shared in this book have been written from my
experience as a leader, a leadership coach, and as a mother
of a little boy who we want to see develop into a leader in his
preferred field, and for him to reach for the stars.

Published in Australia by Ingram Spark
https://www.ingramspark.com

Managing Change

By Renata Roberts
Illustrated by Josefina Luna

TIPS FOR THE READER

Four steps to get the most out of joining Jackson's journey...

1 Before reading Jackson's journey, go to the last page and read the key learnings from this book. Take time to understand them yourself.

2 Now find a comfortable place to take your little learner through the story, reading aloud and talking about what is happening in the pictures.

STEP

3

As you come to the part of the story where a key learning is experienced by Jackson, help your learner to understand this more by reinforcing the importance of the lesson.

STEP

4

At the end, take time to talk through the key learnings again, referring this time to how your little learner might do this themselves.

One day, Jackson and his family woke to their house on fire.

Jackson was so brave
and knew just what he had to do.

He had to take his Mummy's hand and
head out to the front of the house and
wait for the fire fighters to arrive.

Jackson stood and watched the firefighters use their hoses to put the flames out.

The firefighters did a great job. Most of the outside of Jackson's home was still standing when they were done.

But on the inside, there was a lot of damage. All of Jackson's things had been burnt by the fire, blackened by the smoke, or damaged from the water.

Jackson's Mummy and Daddy said that there was no need to be sad because the main thing was that the three of them were safe.

"We will be able to build back our home and buy new things, Jackson," his Daddy said to him that afternoon.

Jackson and his family were lucky to move into a temporary place around the corner from their "burnt home", as Jackson often called it.

Jackson was close enough to still be able to walk to school with his friend when the weather was good.

One day when Jackson was walking Ollie with his Mummy and Daddy, he overheard his parents talking about rebuilding their new home.

"They are able to move that wall to make the room bigger. That will be wonderful for when Jackson is older and has friends over," his Mummy said to his Daddy.

"I don't want a bigger room,"
Jackson said to his Mummy. "I want
the house to be exactly the same as
it was before."

"Jackson," his Mummy said, "the
house isn't going to look exactly the
same. But it will be our home and it
will look beautiful."

Jackson was very concerned and a
little anxious. Jackson wasn't happy
about it having to change.

Jackson ran to the nearby playground and sat at the top of the slide. Daddy went up to join him.

"Jackson, it is ok to be anxious about change. Many people are when things have to change. It is important to remember that while change may be scary, it can be exciting as well," his Daddy said.

Jackson's Daddy explained to him why there needed to be a change in the room, and promised he could be part of all the decisions that had to be made from this moment on.

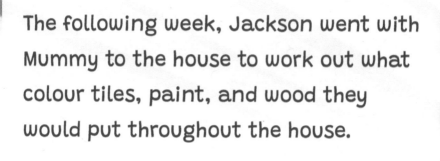

The following week, Jackson went with Mummy to the house to work out what colour tiles, paint, and wood they would put throughout the house.

"What is your favourite, Jackson," Mummy asked. "I like that one," Jackson said pointing to the reddest piece of wood in the pile.

"You know what," Mummy said, "that's my favourite too."

Jackson loved helping with the
changes being made at his home.

"Jackson, what colour do you think your room is going to be?"
Jackson hadn't thought of that before. He was so excited that he could pick.

"Well, my favourite colour is red. So, it has to have red. I think red, green and blue stripes."

Soon Jackson was back in his home, and he LOVED his new room and all the space that the house now had for him to play with his friends.

Jackson realised the change
wasn't that bad after all.

JACKSON'S JOURNEY

These are the KEY LEARNINGS you will find in this journey of Jackson's...

Many people have a tendency to resist change, so it is important to learn how to bring people along to the end goal.

These are some important things you can do:

1. Be clear with WHY things have to change — if you don't understand yourself, ask questions to be clear in your own mind.

2. Talk about it a lot — be open about what is happening, celebrate key steps, give others the chance to ask questions they might have through the change.

3. Accept that anxiety happens — it is ok to not feel comfortable about the change, so talk about how you are feeling with those around you.

4. Make it fun — change may be scary, but it can also bring a lot of exciting opportunities, so try to make the most of it when you can.

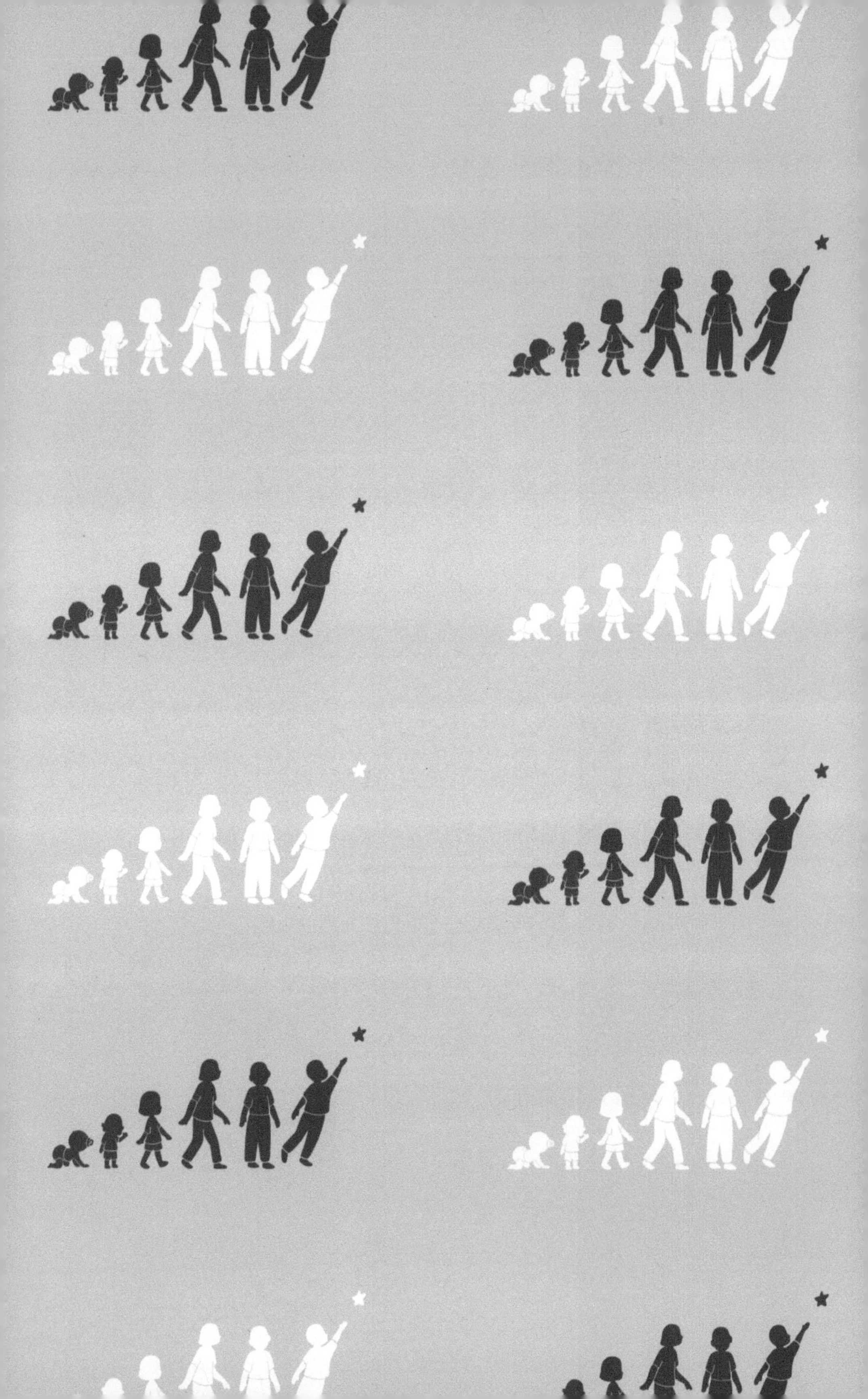

Milton Keynes UK
Ingram Content Group UK Ltd.
UKHW050212300823
427727UK00001B/3